Hurry up, Edward!

Designed by Julie Clough
Series Editor: Teresa Wilson

Thomas the Tank Engine & Friends™

A BRITT ALLCROFT COMPANY PRODUCTION

Based on The Railway Series by The Reverend W Awdry
© 2006 Gullane (Thomas) LLC. A HIT Entertainment Company
Thomas the Tank Engine & Friends and Thomas & Friends are trademarks of Gullane Entertainment Inc.
Thomas the Tank Engine & Friends is Reg. U.S. Pat. & Tm. Off.

First published in Great Britain in 2003
This new edition published in 2006 by Dean,
an imprint of Egmont Books Limited,
239 Kensington High Street, London W8 6SA
Printed in Italy
ISBN 978 0 6035 6224 2
ISBN 0 6035 6224 8

1 3 5 7 9 10 8 6 4 2

Educational consultant: Nicola Morgan, literacy expert and author of over 60 early learning books

Sort and colour

Circle all the things that we use to tell the time.
Now colour them.

Find the correct order

The Fat Controller is a busy man. Look at the **clocks** in **each** picture. Number these pictures 1 to 4, starting **with waking up.**

Odd one out

Draw a line to join the clocks that say the same time.
Colour the odd one out.

O'clock

When the big hand is at the 12, it is something **o'clock**.
Colour the clocks that say something o'clock.

Join the dots

Join the dots from 1 to 20 to make a beautiful station clock.

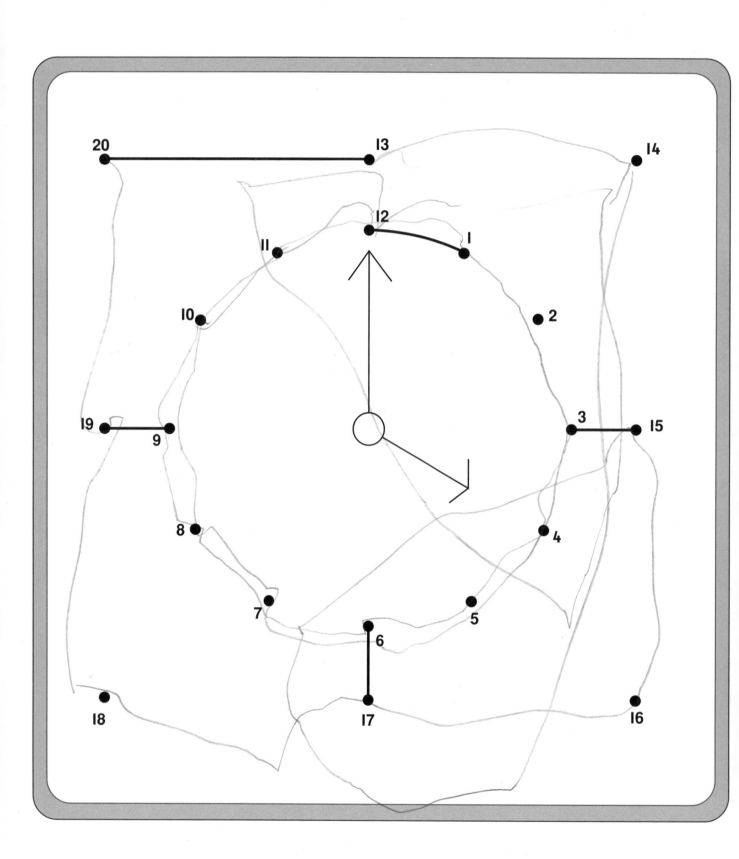

Go through the maze

Help Edward find his way to the party. Pass only the clocks that say something **o'clock**.

Find the correct order

Look at the clocks. Number the pictures 1 to 6 to show the correct order as Edward goes back to the Yard – and to a big surprise!

1

Clock-wise

The hands on a clock always go in the same direction.
This is called **clock-wise** direction.
Find the picture that shows **1 o'clock**
and then number the pictures 1 to 4
to show the engines getting ready
for Edward's party at 4 o'clock.

One hour later

Look at the clock on the left. Circle the clock on the right which is one hour later.

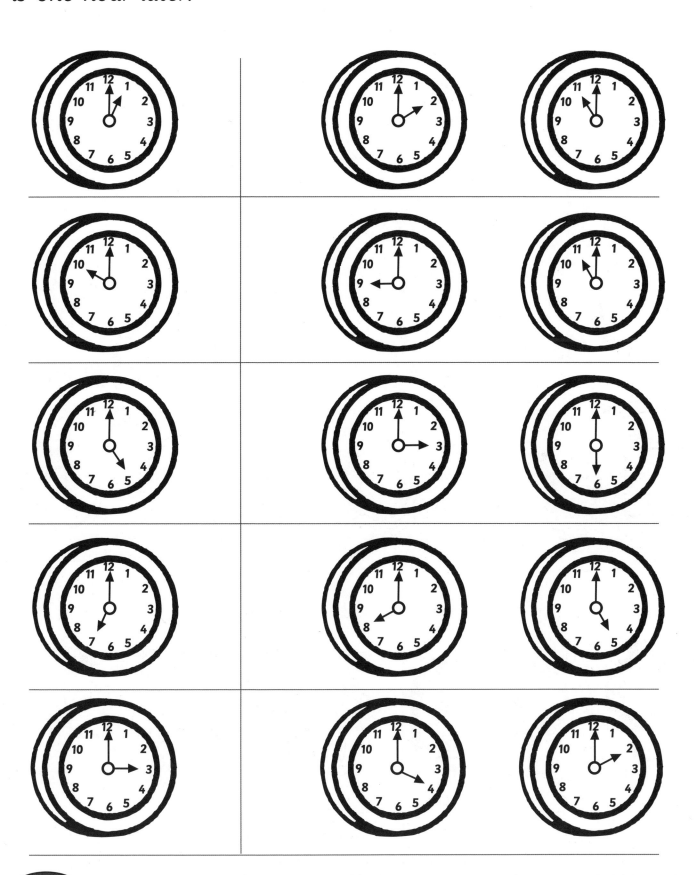

Trace the clocks

Can you recognise the clocks from their descriptions? Read the descriptions. Now trace over the picture that best fits the description and copy it into the box.

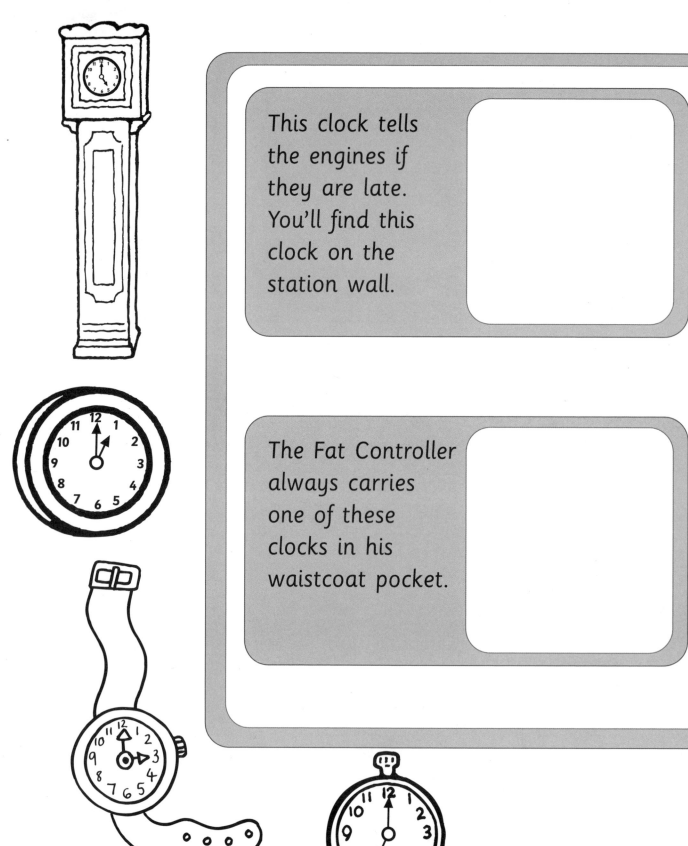

This clock tells the engines if they are late. You'll find this clock on the station wall.

The Fat Controller always carries one of these clocks in his waistcoat pocket.

Draw a line to match the time to the correct clock.

| 3 o'clock | 1 o'clock |

| 5 o'clock | 7 o'clock |

This grand old clock stands on the ground. The Fat Controller has one in his house.

You wear this on your wrist to tell you the time, wherever you are.

One hour earlier

See if you can write an earlier time. Look at the clock on the left. On the clock on the right, draw in the **small hand** so that the clock says one hour earlier.

Find opportunities to put this in context. E.g., say that tea will be at 6 o'clock but we will play outside an hour earlier. Use other words, too, such as **before**, **after**, **first**, **then**, **soon**.

Half-past

When the big hand is at the 6, it is **half-past** something.
Colour the watches that say half-past and read the time.

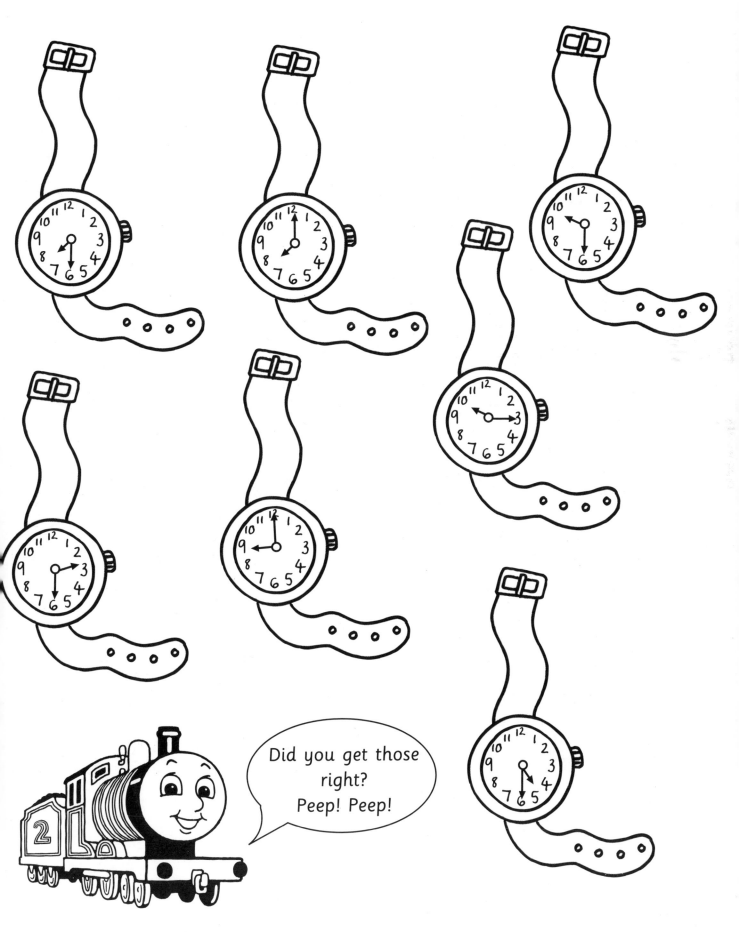

Did you get those right?
Peep! Peep!

Crossword

The answers to this crossword are all to do with **time**. Read the clues. Choose from the words given below. Can you find an extra word in the puzzle?

1. A very small bit of time. There are 60 in one minute.

2. There are 60 minutes in one h _____ .

3. It's not time yet. You are too e _____ .

4. When the big hand is at the 6, it is h _____ - _____ something.

5. If today is Monday, t _____ is Tuesday.

6. 60 seconds make one m _____ .

7. A clock has a big hand and a s _____ hand.

8. Hurry up or you will be l _____ !

late   second   half-past   hour   tomorrow   small   minute   early

1.

2.

3.

4.

5.

6.

7.

8.

Quarter-past

When the big hand is at the 3, it is **quarter-past** something.
All these clocks say quarter-past. Look at the small hand to find
quarter-past what. Draw a line to join matching pairs.

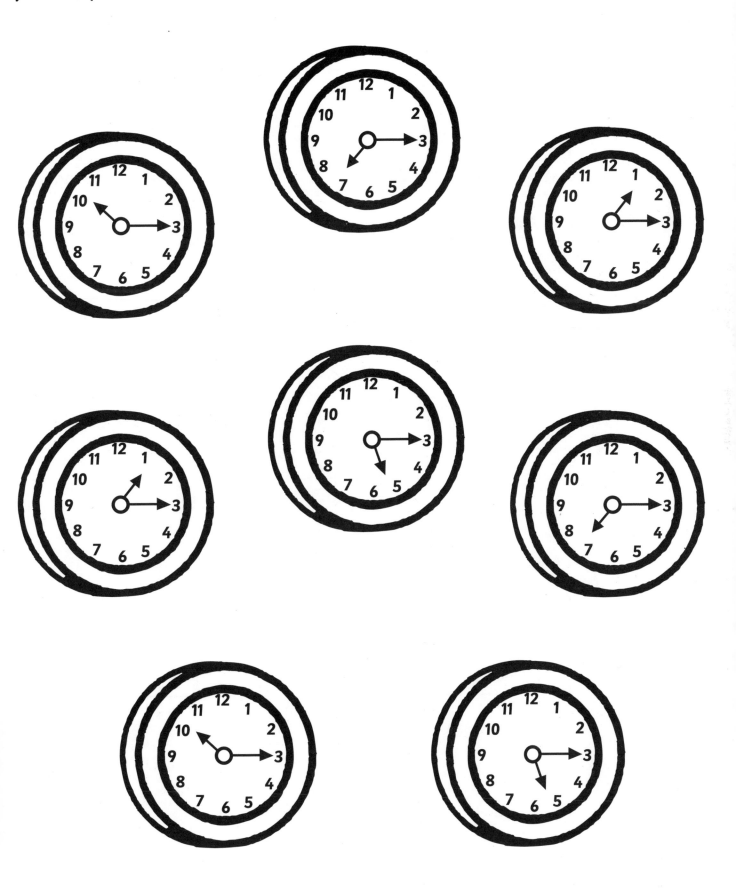

Go through the maze

The engines must get the party ready by 4 o'clock.
Help them find the right way through the maze.
Look at the time on each clock you pass – it should move a bit
further on each time or you've gone the wrong way.

Quarter-to

When the big hand is at the 9, it is **quarter-to** something.
Colour the watch in each line that says quarter-to something.

Draw the big hand

Draw in the big hand to make the correct time.

2 o'clock

quarter-past 2

half-past 2

quarter-to 3

3 o'clock

quarter-past 3

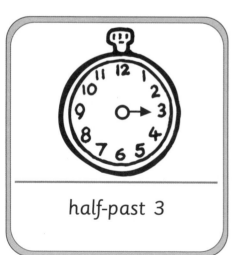

half-past 3

quarter-to 4

4 o'clock

 Most children will need a great deal of practice at exercises like this one. Make some pictures or use a real clock to help your child understand.

Match the time

Tell the time in each picture, and draw a line to match it to the correct time written below.

| quarter-to 1 | 5 o'clock | half-past 2 | quarter-past 10 |

Edward got back at 4 o'clock – just in time for his party! Can you draw hands to show **4 o'clock**?

Game time

Thomas, Henry and Percy have made a game for Edward's party.

Each player takes turns to throw a dice and moves his or her counter that number of spaces. If the player can tell the time correctly, he or she moves an extra **3 spaces** before the next player has a turn.

How to make your engine counters:

Trace over the engine you want to be and transfer onto paper.

Ask a grown-up to help you cut out the engine.

You are now ready to play!

START

FINISH

Notes

Thomas Learning Programme – giving children confidence in early maths concepts

Each activity book has a related story book. Each story book and activity book introduce an aspect of maths. The story book introduces the topic, while the activity book provides practical activities to develop your child's understanding of that topic. While it is not essential to use the story book, by doing so you will increase your child's enjoyment and confidence.

This book, together with its matching story book, 'Hurry up, Edward!', helps your child develop an understanding of the concept of time. The tracing element adds to the fun and helps learning.

This book works on the following skills:
• recognising different clocks
• the language of time
• o'clock, half-past, quarter-past, quarter-to
• earlier/later
• direction of time
• sequence of events

Using the activity books:
• Read the related story first, if you have it. This is not necessary but adds a fun context for the activities.
• Set aside a special time each day and sit comfortably at a table. Don't do too much in one session – be guided by your child.
• Go through the tasks with your child. Give as much help as your child wants.
• Talk about what is on the page and find out which parts your child found easiest or hardest. Make extra examples to help your child.
• Always give lots of praise. The best way to help your child is to make him or her feel confident.